Where's Ou

ar?

Alison Hawes

Illustrated by Sue Reeves

We went out with Mum.
We went in the car.

SHOPPING
CENTRE

Mum parked the car.
We got out.

TO THE SHOPS

We went to the shoe shop.
Mum got some shoes.

PLEASE PAY HERE

We went to the sports shop.
My brother got a helmet.

SALE
SALE · SALE · SA
SALE

We went to the book shop.
I got a book.

Children's books
books
a b c d e
The Rabbit

We went back to the car park.

SALE

“Help!” said Mum.
“I can’t see the car!”

D D
SALE

D
Look! I can see the car.
SALE!